Bond
No.1 for exam success

Maths and Non-verbal Reasoning

Assessment Papers

CEM
(Durham University)

8–9 years

OXFORD
UNIVERSITY PRESS

Great Clarendon Street, Oxford, OX2 6DP, United Kingdom

Oxford University Press is a department of the University of Oxford. It furthers the University's objective of excellence in research, scholarship, and education by publishing worldwide. Oxford is a registered trade mark of Oxford University Press in the UK and in certain other countries

British Library Cataloguing in Publication Data
Data available

978-0-1927-4285-8
10 9 8 7 6 5 4 3 2

Paper used in the production of this book is a natural, recyclable product made from wood grown in sustainable forests. The manufacturing process conforms to the environmental regulations of the country of origin.

Printed in China

Acknowledgements

Page make-up: Tech-Set Ltd, Gateshead
Illustrations: Beehive Illustration
Cover illustrations: Lo Cole

Although we have made every effort to trace and contact all copyright holders before publication this has not been possible in all cases.
If notified, the publisher will rectify any errors or omissions at the earliest opportunity.

Links to third party websites are provided by Oxford in good faith and for information only. Oxford disclaims any responsibility for the materials contained in any third party website referenced in this work.

Before you get started

What is Bond?

This book is part of the Bond CEM Assessment Papers series for Maths and Non-verbal Reasoning, which provides **thorough and continuous practice of key Maths and Non-verbal Reasoning skills** from ages eight to eleven. Bond's resources are ideal preparation for Key Stage 1 and Key Stage 2 SATs, the 11⁺, the CEE and other selective school entrance exams.

How does the scope of this book match real exam content?

Each paper is carefully pitched to ensure a smooth progression towards the next level. Unlike other 11⁺ papers, the CEM exam is a combination of maths **and** non-verbal reasoning questions. They cover numbers, shape and space, measure, algebra, sequences, data and graphs and the key non-verbal reasoning questions. The question format is much more varied and this holistic approach to learning key skills, rather than learning question styles, will also provide a rigorous foundation for other exams.

The coverage of number work, statistics and algebra is matched to the National Curriculum Mathematics Programme of Study and will **provide invaluable preparation for Key Stage 2 SATs**. The aim of the CEM exam is to constantly change the style and format of questions. This makes it outside of the scope of any book to provide a prescriptive series of papers, but the Bond CEM Assessment Papers are based on the range and styles of questions asked in previous exams alongside a solid foundation of the **key skills that will underpin the CEM exams**.

What does the book contain?

- **6 papers** – each with a differing number of questions.
- **Tutorial links throughout** – 📖 – this icon appears in the margin next to the questions. It indicates links to the relevant section in *How To Do CEM Maths and Non-verbal Reasoning*, our invaluable subject guide that offers explanations and practice for all core question types.
- **Scoring devices** – there are score boxes in the margins and a Progress Chart on page 52. The chart is a visual and motivating way for children to see how they are doing. It also turns the score into a percentage that can help inform what to do next.
- **Answers** – located in an easily-removed central pull-out section.

How can you use this book?

One of the great strengths of Bond Assessment Papers is their flexibility. They can be used at home, in school and by tutors to:

- set **timed formal practice** tests – allow about 45 minutes per paper in line with standard 11+ demands. Gradually reduce the suggested time limit by ten minutes to practise working at speed
- provide **bite-sized chunks** for regular practice
- **highlight strengths and weaknesses** in the core skills
- identify **individual needs**
- set **homework**
- follow **a complete 11+ preparation strategy** alongside *The Parents' Guide to the 11+* (see below).

It is best to start at the beginning and work through the papers in order to make the best use of the Progress Chart. If you are using the book as part of a careful run-in to the 11+, we suggest that you also have two other essential Bond resources close at hand:

- *How To Do CEM Maths and Non-verbal Reasoning*: the subject guide that explains all the question types practised in this book. Use the cross-reference icons to find the relevant sections.
- *The Parents' Guide to the 11+*: the step-by-step guide to the whole 11+ experience. It clearly explains the 11+ process, provides guidance on how to assess children, helps you to set complete action plans for practice and explains how you can use *CEM Maths and Non-verbal Reasoning 8-9* as part of a strategic run-in to the exam.

What does a score mean and how can it be improved?

It is unfortunately impossible to guarantee that a child will pass the 11+ exam if they achieve a certain score on any practice book or paper. Success on the day depends on a host of factors, including the scores of the other children sitting the test. However, we can provide invaluable guidance on what a score indicates and how to improve it.

If children colour in the Progress Chart on page 52, this will give an idea of present performance in percentage terms. The Next Steps Planner inside the back cover will help you to decide what to do next to help a child progress. It is always valuable to go over wrong answers with children. If they are having trouble with any particular question type, follow the tutorial links to *How To Do CEM Maths and Non-verbal Reasoning* for step-by-step explanations and further practice. Bond offers the complete range of resources for you and your child, to give you the maximum support that you need.

Don't forget the website ...!

Visit www.bond11plus.co.uk for lots of advice, information and suggestions on everything to do with Bond, the 11+ and helping children to achieve their best.

Key words

Some special words and symbols are used in this book. You will find them in **bold** each time they appear in the Papers. These words are explained here.

<	sign meaning 'is less than'
>	sign meaning 'is greater than'
area	the surface of a shape measured in square units, for example square cm, which can be written as cm^2
cube	a 3D solid shape with each face an identical square and side faces that are perpendicular to the end faces
decimal	common way to refer to a number that has parts less than one that are expressed using a decimal point, for example one-half is 0.5
difference	the difference between two numbers is found by subtracting the smaller number from the larger number
digit	0, 1, 2, 3, 4, 5, 6, 7, 8 and 9 are all digits
edge	the line along which two adjacent faces of a solid shape meet
faces	any surface of a 3D solid is a face
fraction	expressing one number as a part of another number forms a fraction, for example one out of two is one-half (written as $\frac{1}{2}$)
hexagon	a polygon with 6 sides and 6 angles
multiple	a multiple is the product of a number multiplied by another whole number, for example 12 is a multiple of 6
net	a series of adjoining 2D shapes that will fold up together to form a 3D solid
perimeter	the distance around the edge of a 2D shape
quadrilateral	a 2D polygon with 4 sides and 4 angles
quarter	one-fourth of a whole
right angle	a square angle or corner measuring 90 degrees exactly
rounding	to round a number is to take the number to the nearest ten, or hundred (and so on) as asked for; remember to increase the value by 1 if the digit immediately to the right of that column is 5 or more
tally chart	a method of recording data using short lines, one for each object or count, grouped into 5s for easy addition
total	added all together
vertices	corners

Paper 1

Fill in the missing numbers:

1 57 + 14 + ___29___ = 100

2 1000 − 325 = 600 + ___74___ 75

3 4 × 3 × 10 = ___120___

4 30 × 50 = ___1500___ ÷ 2

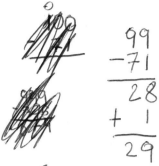

```
  99
 -71
 ----
  28
 + 1
 ----
  29
```

5 What number comes next?

a $4\frac{1}{2}$, 6, $7\frac{1}{2}$, 9, ___$10\frac{1}{2}$___   **b**   46, 38, 30, 22, _____

6 Draw a line between each **fraction** and its correct diagram. The first one has been done for you:

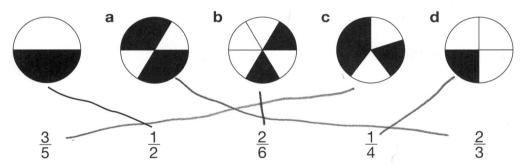

$\frac{3}{5}$ $\frac{1}{2}$ $\frac{2}{6}$ $\frac{1}{4}$ $\frac{2}{3}$

7 Underline the numbers that are **multiples** of 3:

360   471   23   35   150   41   81

8 Write the following **decimal** numbers in **digits**:

a four hundred and two and four hundredths _____

b seven hundred and two thousand, seventy-two and seven tenths

_____

9 If $a = 5$, solve the following equations:

a $3a + 10 =$ _____   **b** $96 − 7a =$ _____

10 How many flat **faces** are there on a cylinder and what shape are they?

2 circles ✓

11 Fill in the three missing numbers in this number chain:

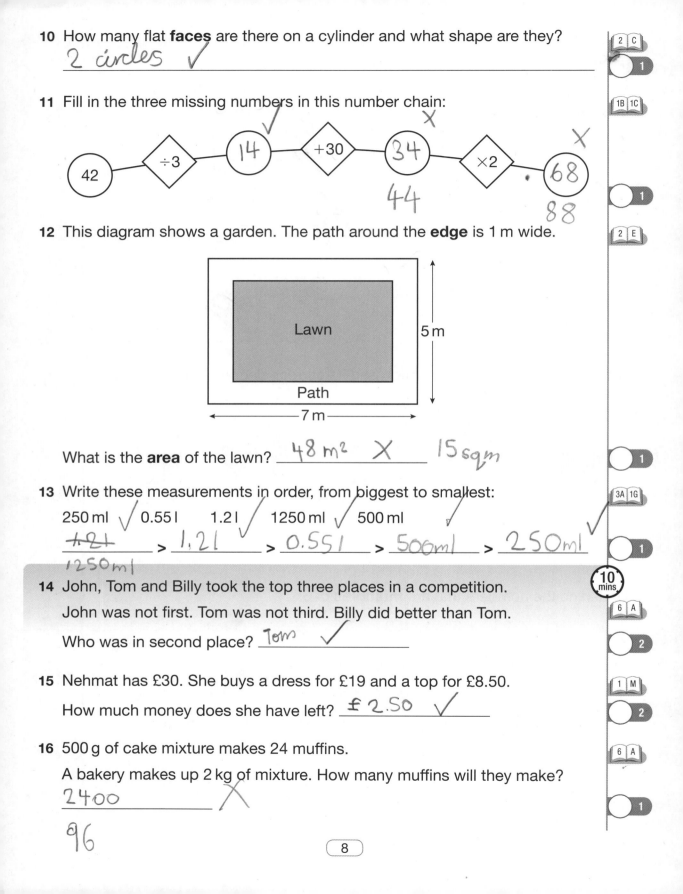

42 → ÷3 → 14 ✓ → +30 → 34 ✗ → ×2 → 68 ✗

44

88

12 This diagram shows a garden. The path around the **edge** is 1 m wide.

Lawn   5 m

Path

7 m

What is the **area** of the lawn? 48 m² ✗   15 sqm

13 Write these measurements in order, from biggest to smallest:

250 ml ✓   0.55 l   1.2 l ✓   1250 ml ✓   500 ml ✓

~~1.2 l~~ > 1.2 l ✓ > 0.55 l > 500 ml > 250 ml ✓

1250 ml

14 John, Tom and Billy took the top three places in a competition.

John was not first. Tom was not third. Billy did better than Tom.

Who was in second place? Tom ✓

15 Nehmat has £30. She buys a dress for £19 and a top for £8.50.

How much money does she have left? £ 2.50 ✓

16 500 g of cake mixture makes 24 muffins.

A bakery makes up 2 kg of mixture. How many muffins will they make?

2400 ✗

96

17 Dale has three letters to post. One will cost 49p, one will cost 82p and the third one will cost £1.25.

a How much does he need altogether? _£2.56_ ✓

b How much change will he get from a £10 note? _£7.44_ ✓

18 This table shows the weekly opening times of a shop:

Sunday	Closed
Monday	9:00 am – 5:00 pm
Tuesday	10:00 am – 6:00 pm
Wednesday	9:00 am – 1:00 pm
Thursday	8:00 am – 5:00 pm
Friday	8:30 am – 4:30 pm
Saturday	9:00 am – 12:00 noon

8h
8h
4h
9h
8h
3h

$$\begin{array}{r} 49p \\ +82p \\ £1.25 \\ \hline 2.56 \end{array}$$

a What is the earliest time the shop opens? _8 am_ ✓

b On which day is the shop open latest in the evening?

Tuesday ✓

c On which day of the week is the shop open for the longest length of time? _Thursday_ ✓

d During one whole week, for how many hours is the shop open in **total**?

40 hours ✓

19 Use the information in this **tally chart** to plot the bar chart.

Red	|||| |||| ||	Green	|||| ||
Blue	|||| |||	Yellow	|||| ||||

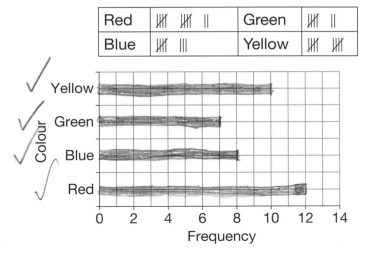

Which shape or pattern on the right belongs to the group on the left?
Underline the answer.

Example

  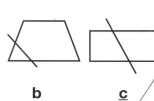

a   b   <u>c</u>   d   e

20

  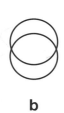 

a   b   c   d   e

21

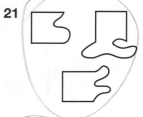

a   b   c   d   e

22

a   b   c   d   e

3

Which shape completes the second pair in the same way as the first pair?
Underline the answer.

Example

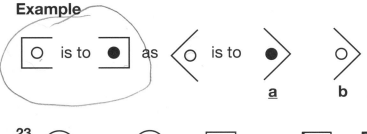

23

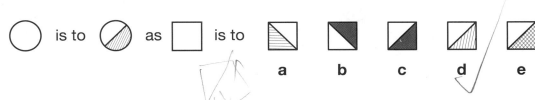

24

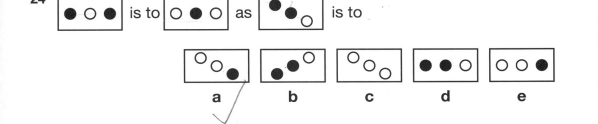

25

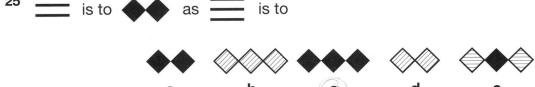

Which one comes next? Underline the answer.

Example

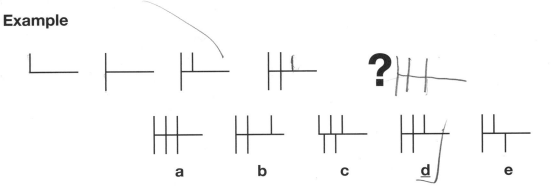

26

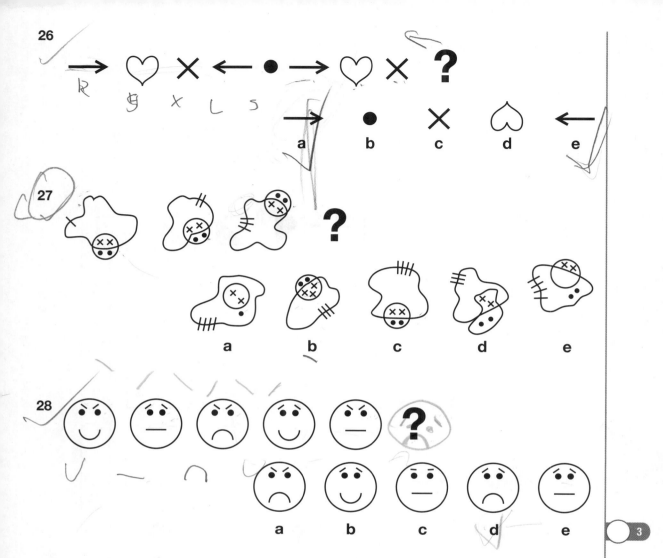

27

28

Which pattern completes the larger shape or grid? Underline the answer.

Example

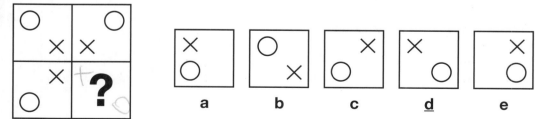

29

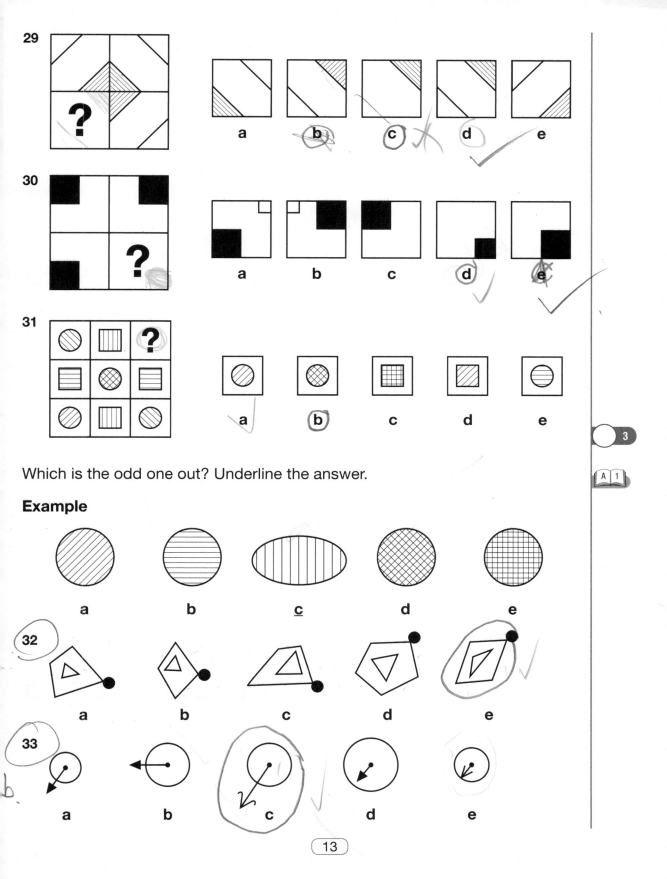

a   b   c   d   e

30

a   b   c   d   e

31

a   b   c   d   e

3

A 1

Which is the odd one out? Underline the answer.

Example

a   b   <u>c</u>   d   e

32

a   b   c   d   e

33

a   b   c   d   e

13

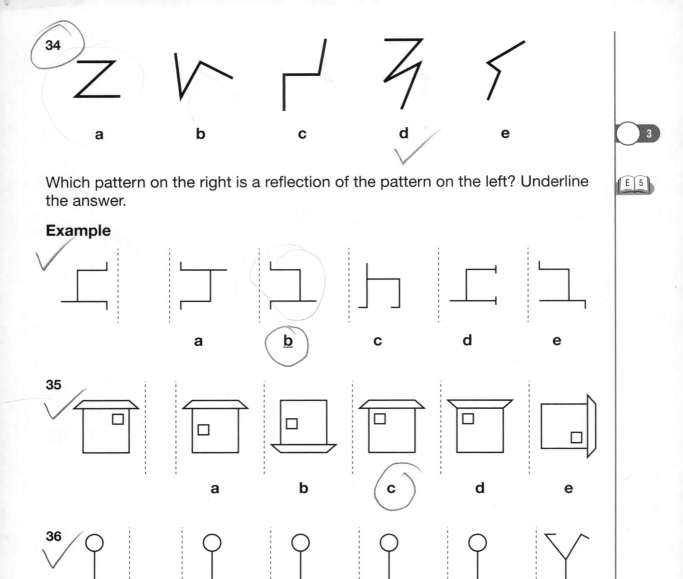

34

a b c d e

3

Which pattern on the right is a reflection of the pattern on the left? Underline the answer.

E 5

Example

a **b** c d e

35

a b c d e

36

a b c d e

2

Now go to the Progress Chart to record your score! Total 45

Paper 2

1 Natalie's jam recipe uses twice as much sugar as raspberries.

Natalie uses 3 kg of raspberries to make some jam. The recipe says to add 500 ml of water for each kg of raspberries. Each kg of sugar will produce 2 jars of jam.

a What weight of sugar does Natalie need? _____

b How much water does Natalie have to add? _____

c How many jars of jam will this mixture make? _____

2 This graph records how many children selected each fruit as one of their favourites.

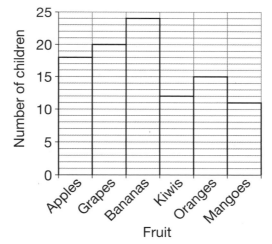

a Which fruit was most popular? _____

b Which was the least popular? _____

c How many children chose grapes? _____

d How many more chose apples than oranges? _____

3 Jo is younger than Tim. Tim is older than Paul. Ben is younger than Jo and Paul.

Who is the eldest of the four boys? _____

4 A lorry driver leaves home at 5:15 am.

He drives for $3\frac{1}{2}$ hours, then has a 1 hour break at the service station.

He sets off again and covers the last 120 miles in 2 hours.

a At what time does he stop at the service station? _____

b What is his average speed in miles per hour for the second part of his

journey? _____

3B 3C

2

5 Look carefully at this table to answer the following questions:

7 A

	Likes dogs		Doesn't like dogs	
Likes cats	Julie		Taya	
Doesn't like cats	Ted		Ray	

a Who likes cats but not dogs? _____

b Who likes cats and dogs? _____

c Add these children's names to the table in the correct places:

Ben – likes cats but not dogs   Asher – doesn't like cats or dogs

Bill – likes dogs but not cats   Aman – likes cats and dogs

4

Which is the odd one out? Underline the answer.

20 mins

A 1

Example

    a   b   c   d   e

6

    a   b   c   d   e

7

    a   b   c   d   e

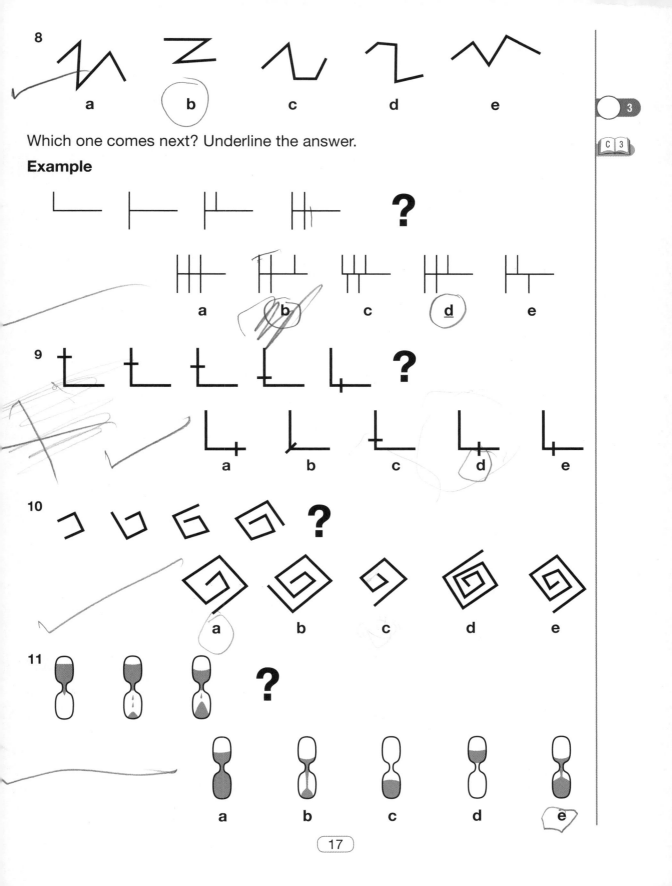

8

a   b   c   d   e

Which one comes next? Underline the answer.

Example

a   b   c   **d**   e

9

a   b   c   d   e

10

a   b   c   d   e

11

a   b   c   d   e

17

12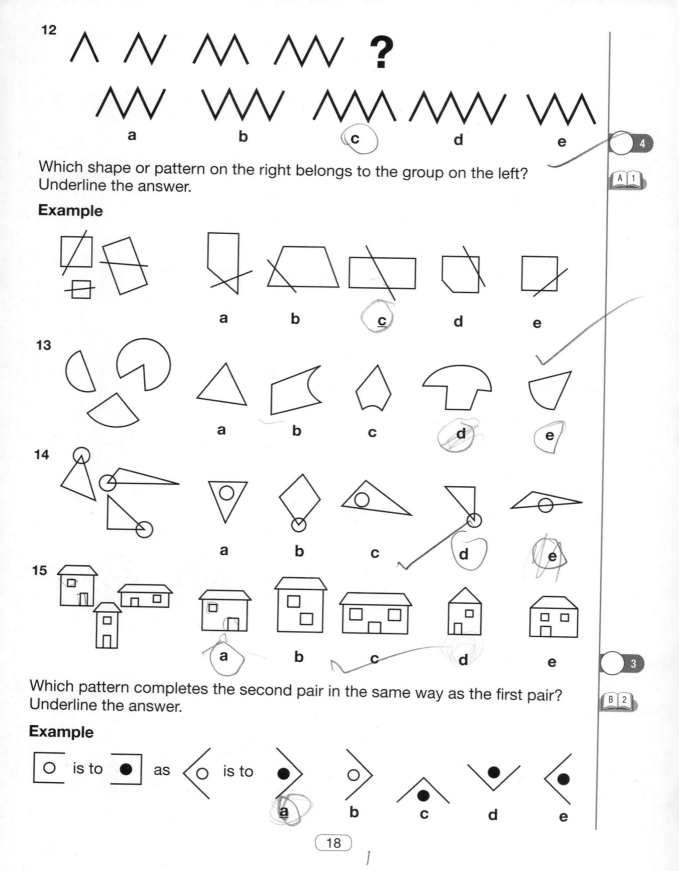

∧ ∧/ ∧∧ ∧∧/ ∧∧∧/ **?**

∧∧∧/   ∨∧∧∧   ∧∧∧∧   ∧∧∧∧/   ∧∧∧
a   **b**   **c**   **d**   **e**

Which shape or pattern on the right belongs to the group on the left?
Underline the answer.

Example

a   **b**   <u>**c**</u>   **d**   **e**

13

a   **b**   **c**   **d**   **e**

14

a   **b**   **c**   **d**   **e**

15

a   **b**   **c**   **d**   **e**

Which pattern completes the second pair in the same way as the first pair?
Underline the answer.

Example

○ is to ● as ⟨○ is to

a   **b**   **c**   **d**   **e**

18

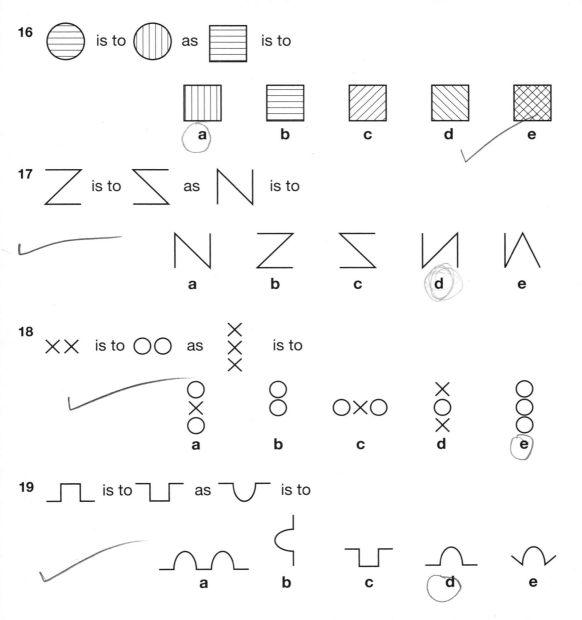

16 ⊖ is to ⊕ as ▤ is to

a   b   c   d   e

17 Z is to Σ as И is to

a   b   c   d   e

18 ✕✕ is to ○○ as ✕✕✕ is to

a   b   c   d   e

19 ⊓ is to ⊓ as ⊔ is to

a   b   c   d   e

Which code matches the shape or pattern given at the end of each line?
Underline the answer.

Example

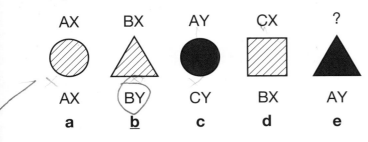

AX	BX	AY	CX	?
AX	BY	CY	BX	AY
a	**b**	c	d	e

20

AM	BM	BN	CM	?AN

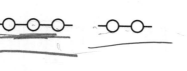

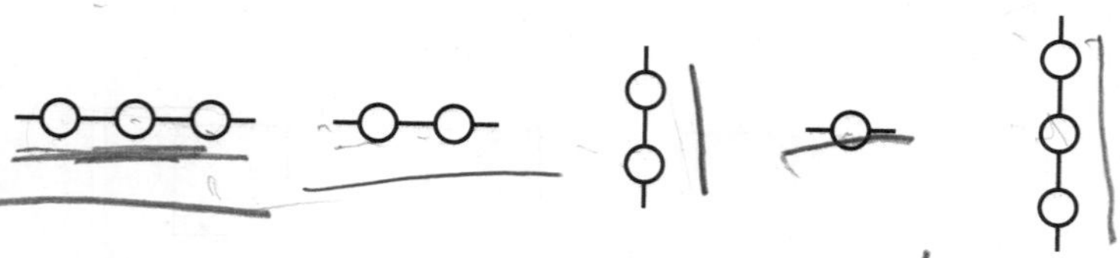

CN	AM	BM	AN	BN
a	**b**	**c**	**d**	**e**

21

AX	AY	CZ	CX	?

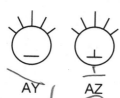

AY	AZ	CY	CX	CZ
a	**b**	**c**	**d**	**e**

22

AL	CL	AR	BL	?

 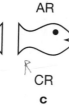 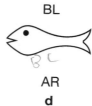

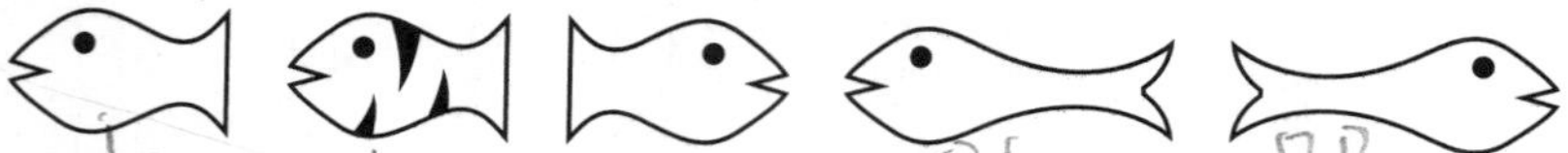

BR	BL	CR	AR	CL
a	**b**	**c**	**d**	**e**

Complete these number chains:

23 4 → × 3 then + 4 → _____

24 11 → × 2 then – 7 → _____

25 Write the number fifteen thousand and fifteen in **digits**.

_____

26 Shade in the **fraction** of each shape:

Example

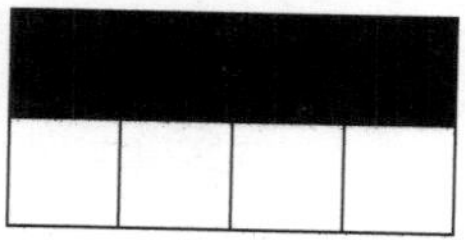

$\frac{1}{2}$

a

$\frac{1}{3}$

b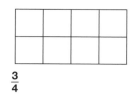

$\frac{3}{4}$

c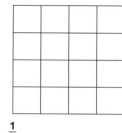

$\frac{1}{8}$

44 + 25 = 6a

3

27 Complete these triplets so that they add up to 100.

1 B

a 44 + 25 + _____

c 74 + 20 + _____

b 18 + 60 + _____

d 35 + 31 + _____

2

28 Complete this grid describing 2D shapes:

2 B

Shape	Number of angles	Must it have right angles?	Number of sides
Rectangle			
Octagon			
Triangle			
Hexagon			

4

29 Order these numbers from smallest to largest:

1 G

0.1   100   10.1   10.01   100.1   0.01

_____ < _____ < _____ < _____ < _____ < _____

2

30 What are the missing numbers in each of these number pattern chains?

5 A

a 8, 12, 16, 20, 24, _____, _____

b 64, 56, 48, _____, _____

c 319, 309, _____, 289, 279, _____

d 76, 71, _____, 61, _____ 51

2

Paper 3

1 350 − 174 = _____

2 12 × _____ = 72

3 What is half of 300? _____

4 How many centimetres are there in 1.5 metres? _____

5 How many metres are there in 3 kilometres? _____

6 A programme starts at 10:45 and ends at 11:20. How long does the programme last? _____

7 What numbers come next in these number pattern chains?

   a 105, 110, 115, 120, _____, _____

   b 36, 33, 30, 27, 24, _____, _____

8 What is the name of a six-sided shape? _____

9 Which of these **nets** can be folded up to make a **cube**? _____

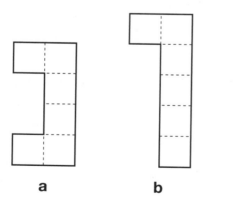

    a   **b**   **c**

10 Add < or > between these pairs of numbers to show which one is greater:

   368 _____ 386   1021 _____ 1212   647 _____ 764   9954 _____ 9939

Which pattern completes the second pair in the same way as the first pair?
Underline the answer.

Example

11

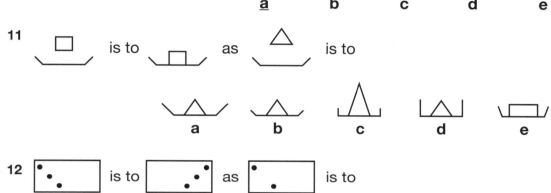

12

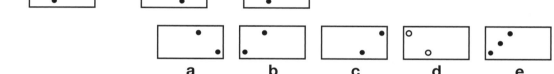

13

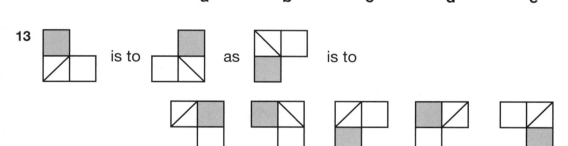

3

Which pattern completes the larger shape or grid? Underline the answer.

Example

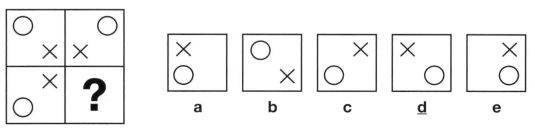

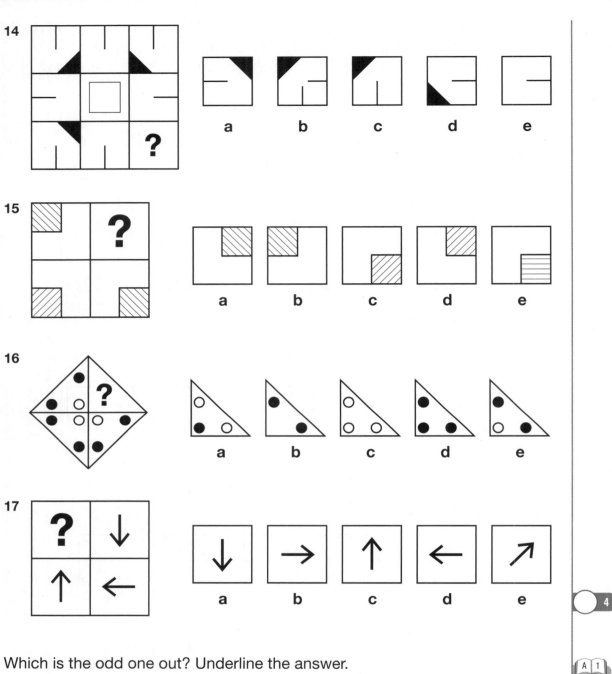

14

a   b   c   d   e

15

a   b   c   d   e

16

a   b   c   d   e

17

a   b   c   d   e

4
A 1

Which is the odd one out? Underline the answer.

Example

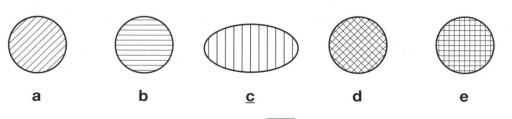

a   b   <u>c</u>   d   e

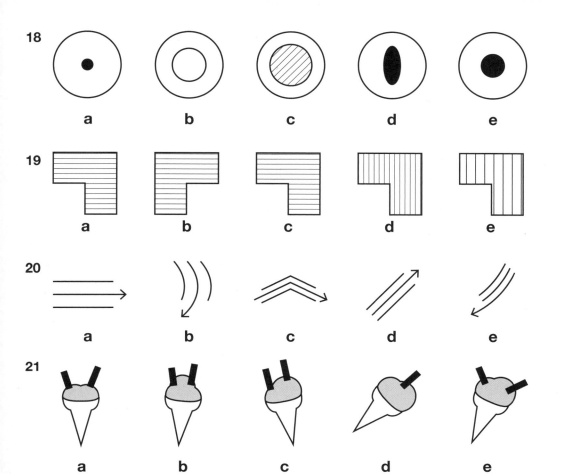

18   a   b   c   d   e

19   a   b   c   d   e

20   a   b   c   d   e

21   a   b   c   d   e

Which shape or pattern on the right belongs to the group on the left?
Underline the answer.

Example

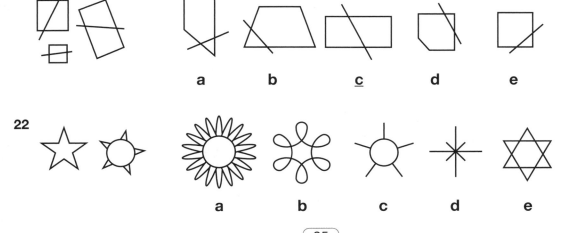

a   b   <u>c</u>   d   e

22

a   b   c   d   e

23

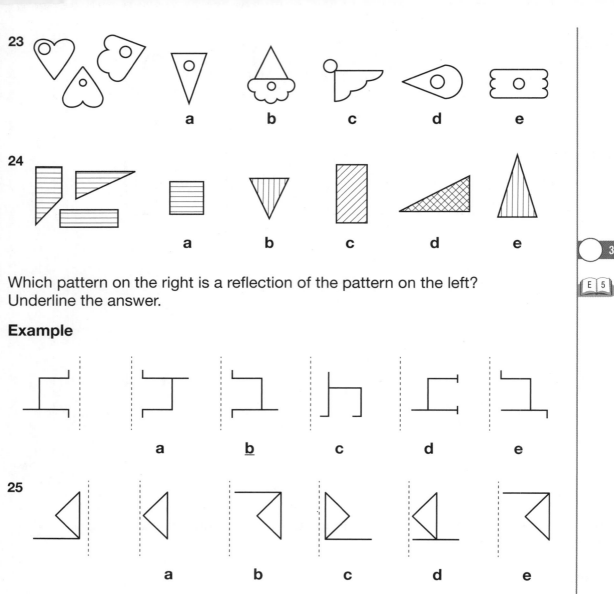

a b c d e

24

a b c d e

Which pattern on the right is a reflection of the pattern on the left?
Underline the answer.

Example

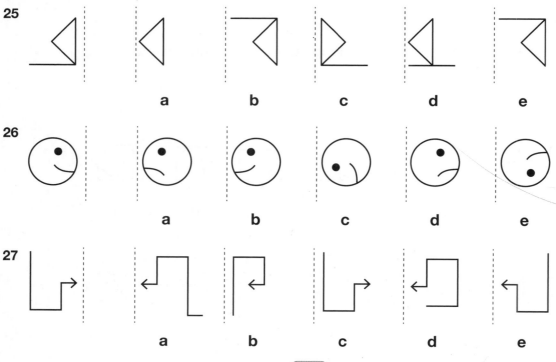

a **b** c d e

25

a b c d e

26

a b c d e

27

a b c d e

26

Paper 1

1 29
2 75
3 120
4 3000
5 a $10\frac{1}{2}$
  b 14
6 ($\frac{1}{2}$ *mark each*)
  a $\frac{2}{3}$
  b $\frac{2}{6}$
  c $\frac{3}{5}$
  d $\frac{1}{4}$
7 360, 471, 150, 81
8 a 402.04
  b 702,072.7
9 a 25
  b 61
10 2 circles
11 14, 44, 88
12 15 sq m
13 1250 ml > 1.2 l > 0.55l > 500 ml > 250 ml
14 Tom
15 £2.50
16 96
17 a £2.56
  b £7.44
18 ($\frac{1}{2}$ *mark each*)
  a 8 am
  b Tuesday
  c Thursday
  d 40 hours
19

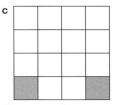

20 d
21 b
22 c
23 d
24 a
25 c
26 e
27 c
28 d
29 d
30 e
31 a
32 d
33 b
34 d
35 c
36 c

Paper 2

1 a 6 kg
  b 1500 ml (or $1\frac{1}{2}$ l)
  c 12 jars
2 ($\frac{1}{2}$ *mark each*)
  a bananas
  b mangoes
  c 20
  d 3
3 Tim
4 a 8:45
  b 60 mph
5 a Taya
  b Julie
  c (*2 marks*)

	Likes dogs		Doesn't like dogs	
Likes cats	Julie	**Aman**	Taya	**Ben**
Doesn't like cats	Ted	**Bill**	Ray	**Asher**

6 c
7 d
8 b
9 d
10 a
11 e
12 c
13 e
14 d
15 a
16 a
17 d
18 e
19 d
20 d
21 c
22 a
23 16
24 15
25 15,015
26 a

(*Any 4 squares*)

  b

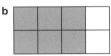

(*Any 6 squares*)

c

(*Any squares*)
27 ($\frac{1}{2}$ *mark each*)
  a 31
  b 22
  c 6
  d 34
28

	Number of angles	Must it have right angles?	Number of sides?
Rectangle	4	Yes	4
Octagon	8	No	8
Triangle	3	No (Can do)	3
Hexagon	6	No	6

29 0.01 < 0.1 < 10.01 < 10.1 < 100 < 100.1
30 a 28, 32
  b 40, 32
  c 299, 269
  d 66, 56

Paper 3

1 176
2 6
3 150
4 150 cm
5 3000 mm
6 35 minutes
7 a 125, 130
  b 21, 18
8 hexagon
9 c
10 368 < 386
    1021 < 1212
    647 < 764
    9954 > 9939
11 b
12 c
13 e
14 c
15 d
16 e
17 b
18 d
19 b
20 e

21 d
22 c
23 d
24 a
25 c
26 b
27 e
28 e
29 c
30 b
31 a
32 a $1\frac{1}{2}$ cm (or 1.5 cm)
   b day 5
   c 6 cm
33 a 30
   b 4
   c February and May
34 a £10.85
   b £1.30
   c £112.10
35 10
36 a £11
   b 2

Paper 4

1 d
2 e
3 a
4 c
5 b
6 e
7 b
8 a
9 b
10 e
11 d
12 a
13 c
14 e
15 a
16 d
17 e
18 d
19 e
20 c
21 e
22 26
23 3
24 35
25 72, 24

26

27 a 2
   b 7
   c –
   d 6
   e 3
   f 9

13	+	2	=	15
–		+		–
7	–	1	=	6
=		=		=
6	+	3	=	9

28 70, 50, 40, 130, 390
29 a $\frac{3}{6} = \frac{2}{4} = \frac{4}{8}$
   b $\frac{2}{10} = \frac{20}{100} = \frac{1}{5}$
   c $\frac{6}{8} = \frac{3}{4} = \frac{30}{40}$
30 ($\frac{1}{2}$ mark each)
   a 340 cm
   b 200 g
   c 75 minutes
   d 3.5 l (or $3\frac{1}{2}$ l)
31 a 30
   b $\frac{1}{2}$
   c 2 orange, 2 lemon, 1 blackberry, 3 apple
32 a 53
   b 33 ($\frac{1}{2}$ mark)
   c 20 ($\frac{1}{2}$ mark)
33 a 20
   b Tue, Wed, Sat
34 a Saturday ($\frac{1}{2}$ mark)
   b 5 ($\frac{1}{2}$ mark)
   c Friday afternoon
   d afternoon

Paper 5

1 6
2 13
3 81
4 100
5 ($\frac{1}{2}$ mark each)
   a 500
   b 200
   c 3000
   d 3600
6 Lines should link $\frac{1}{2}$ to $\frac{6}{12}$; $\frac{3}{4}$ to $\frac{75}{100}$; $\frac{7}{10}$ to 0.7; $\frac{1}{4}$ to 0.25
7 ($\frac{1}{2}$ mark each)
   a 27
   b 124
   c 60
   d 25
8 ($\frac{1}{2}$ mark each)
   a 2000 m
   b 5 m
   c 3.5 m
   d 40 m
9 46 cm
10 Tick inside angle a and angle d
11 11:06, 11:28
12 £40
13 b
14 e
15 b
16 c
17 d
18 b
19 d
20 c
21 b
22 b
23 b
24 a
25 d
26 c
27 b
28 a
29 a 120 cm (or 1.2 m)
   b 30 cm
   c 40 cm
30 a 20 days
   b 30 g
31 a 27
   b 13
32 a 60
   b 46
   c 100
33 ($\frac{1}{2}$ mark each)
   a 5
   b 2
   c 7
   d 3
   e 4
   f 6

1 125
2 4
3 16
4 43
5 18 cm
6 1425 ml
7 4.58 < 4.59 < 4.84 < 5.01 < 5.10
8 3800, 9500, 5100, 10,000
9 a 76
b 44
10 6, 12, 8
11 1 hour 13 minutes 30 seconds
12 a 9 mm $(\frac{1}{2}$ mark)
b Week 3 $(\frac{1}{2}$ mark)
c 3 weeks
d 37 mm

13 $(\frac{1}{2}$ mark each)
a 8:40
b 8:48
c 9:02
d 9:10
14 a 6
b 30
c $\frac{1}{4}$ (a quarter)
15 a 4.4 m (or 440 cm)
b 4.8 m (or 480 cm)
16 a 10 cm
b 5 hours
c 9:30 pm
17 e
18 c
19 d
20 e
21 a

22 a
23 d
24 b
25 e
26 a
27 c
28 d
29 a
30 b
31 c
32 a
33 d
34 e

Which one comes next? Underline the answer.

Example

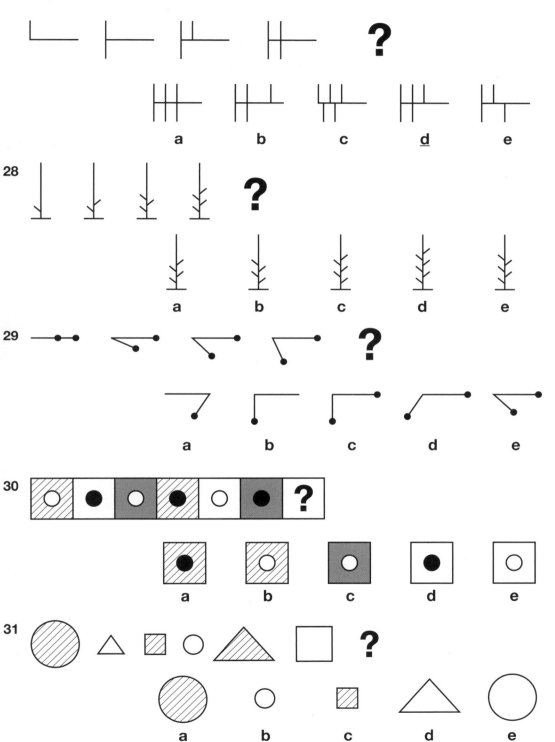

27

4

32 This graph shows how a seedling grows during the first week after its germination, when it is just showing above the soil.

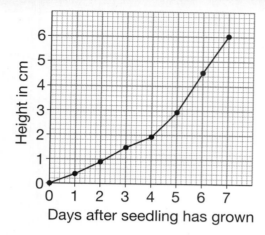

Days after seedling has grown

a What was the height of the seedling on day 3? _____

b On which day did it reach 3 cm? _____

c How tall was the seedling after 7 days? _____

3

33 This table shows the months in which children in a class have their birthday.

7 A

January	3	July	1
February	5	August	1
March	1	September	3
April	2	October	2
May	5	November	3
June	2	December	2

a If the data is for a whole class, how many children are there in the class? _____

b How many more birthdays are there in May than August?

_____

c Which are the most common birthday months? _____

3

34 Mrs Townsend's weekly shop came to £108.50.

1I 1L

a One-tenth of the bill was spent on meat. How much did she spend on

meat? _____

b At the checkout, Dilli added some sweets to the basket, increasing the **total** to £109.80.

What was the price of the sweets? _____

c She bought 4 items on special offer, each for half price, saving £3.60 in **total**.

Without the special offers, and without Dilli's sweets, what would

Mrs Townsend's bill have been? _____

○ 3

35 Tom has a mental maths test every day with marks out of 10.

6 A

On the first day one week he gets 7 out of 10, on the second day he gets 9 out of 10.

His **total** number of marks after 5 days is 46.

How many marks out of ten did he get on the last day? _____

○ 2

36 Marco is given a £25 voucher for his birthday. He goes to buy some DVDs. Some cost £3.50 and others are £4.99.

1 L

a If he buys 4 DVDs at £3.50, how much money will he have left on the

voucher? _____

b How many of the £4.99 DVDs can he then buy at the same time?

_____

○ 2

Now go to the Progress Chart to record your score! **Total** ○ 45

Paper 4

Which is the odd one out? Underline the answer.

Example

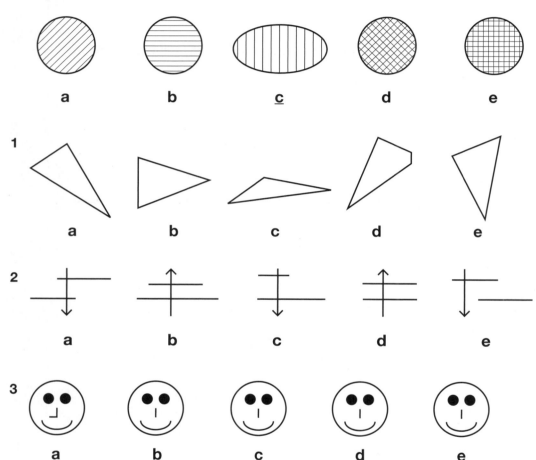

Which code matches the shape or pattern given at the end of each line?
Underline the answer.

Example

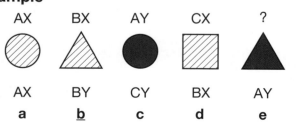

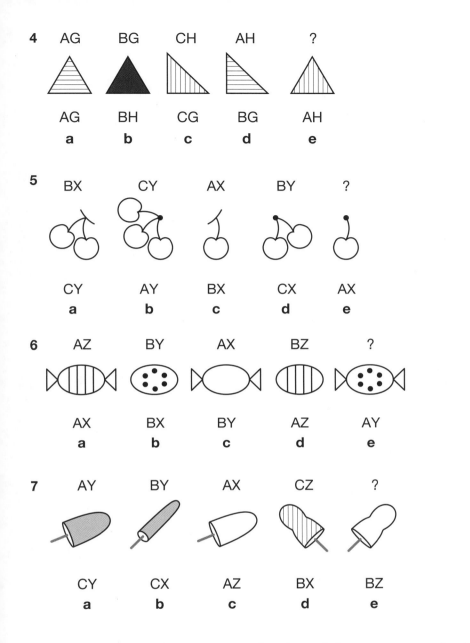

4

AG	BG	CH	AH	?

AG	BH	CG	BG	AH
a	**b**	**c**	**d**	**e**

5

BX	CY	AX	BY	?

CY	AY	BX	CX	AX
a	**b**	**c**	**d**	**e**

6

AZ	BY	AX	BZ	?

AX	BX	BY	AZ	AY
a	**b**	**c**	**d**	**e**

7

AY	BY	AX	CZ	?

CY	CX	AZ	BX	BZ
a	**b**	**c**	**d**	**e**

Which pattern on the right is a reflection of the pattern on the left?
Underline the answer.

Example

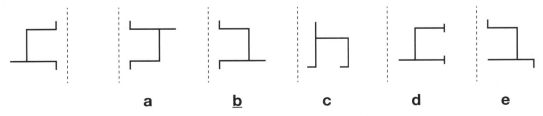

a	<u>b</u>	c	d	e

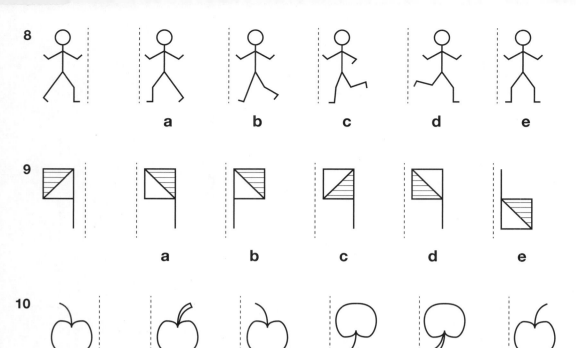

8

a b c d e

9

a b c d e

10

a b c d e

Which one comes next? Underline the answer.

Example

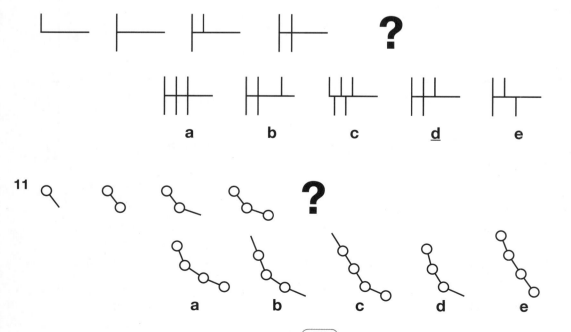

a b c <u>d</u> e

11

a b c d e

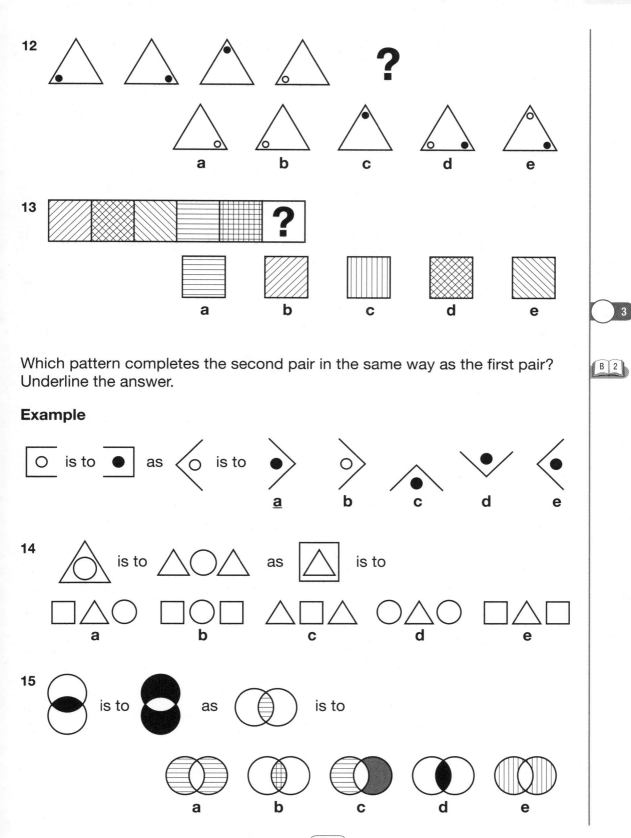

12

13

Which pattern completes the second pair in the same way as the first pair?
Underline the answer.

Example

○ is to ● as ◁○ is to

    a   **b**   **c**   **d**   **e**

14

15

33

16

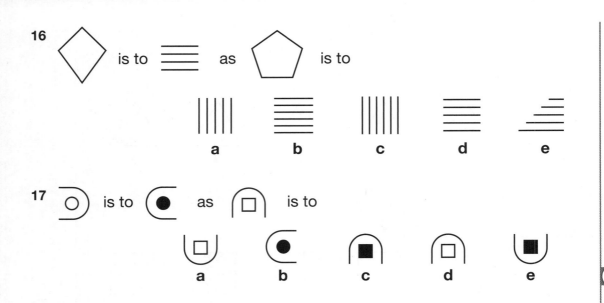

17

Which shape or pattern on the right belongs to the group on the left?
Underline the answer.

Example

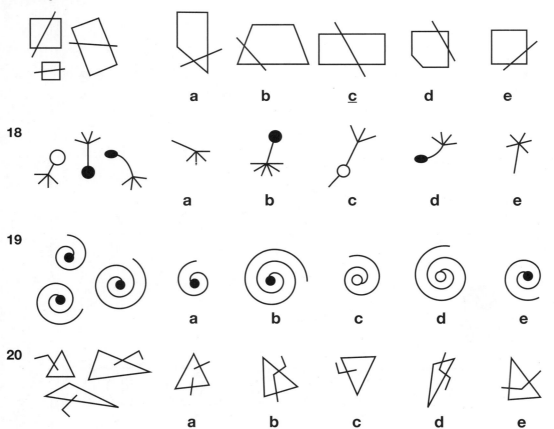

21

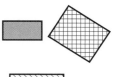

           a   **b**   **c**   **d**   **e**

Fill in the missing numbers:

22 $24 + $ _____ $= 50$

23 $33 + 14 = 50 - $ _____

24 $4 + 11 + $ _____ $= 50$

25 Underline the numbers that are **multiples** of 3:

    34   61   72   24   13

26 Draw a **quadrilateral** with one **right angle**.

27 Complete the missing numbers and symbols in this grid so that the sums going across and the sums going down are correct.

13	+	**a**	=	15
−		+		−
b	**c**	1	=	**d**
=		=		=
6	+	**e**	=	**f**

a _____   c _____   e _____

b _____   d _____   f _____

28 **Round** the following numbers to the nearest ten.

    68   51   39   127   392

29 Fill in the boxes to complete these **fractions**:

a $\dfrac{3}{\boxed{}} = \dfrac{2}{4} = \dfrac{\boxed{}}{8}$

b $\dfrac{2}{10} = \dfrac{\boxed{}}{100} = \dfrac{1}{\boxed{}}$

c $\dfrac{6}{8} = \dfrac{3}{\boxed{}} = \dfrac{\boxed{}}{40}$

30 a How many centimetres are there in 3.4 metres? _____

   b How many grams are there in 0.2 kg? _____

   c How many minutes are there in $1\frac{1}{4}$ hours? _____

   d How many litres do you get from 3500 ml? _____

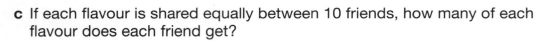

31 There are 80 sweets in a bag. One-**quarter** are orange, 20 are lemon, 10 are blackberry and the rest are apple.

   a How many apple flavoured sweets are there? _____

   b What proportion of the whole bag is made up of orange and lemon sweets? _____

   c If each flavour is shared equally between 10 friends, how many of each flavour does each friend get?

   orange _____   lemon _____

   blackberry _____   apple _____

32 Lionel adds 13 red marbles to his collection.
He now has 66 marbles in **total**.

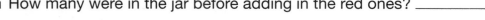

   a How many were in the jar before adding in the red ones? _____

Of the new **total**, half are blue and the rest are white or red.

   b How many are blue? _____

   c How many are white? _____

33 The chart below shows the number of pairs of different types of socks that pass through a boarding school laundry each week for a group of boys.

	Sun	Mon	Tue	Wed	Thur	Fri	Sat
Grey		20	20	20	20	20	20
Sports	12	15	20	20	10	10	20
Coloured	20	2	4	3	3	20	20

a Each boy wears a clean pair of grey socks each weekday. How many

boys are in the group? _____

b If each boy wears a clean pair of sports socks for any games sessions, on which days do all the boys have a games session?

_____

2

34 The chart below records when there was any rainfall at different times during a week.

	Sun	Mon	Tue	Wed	Thur	Fri	Sat
Morning	✓		✓		✓	✓	
Afternoon	✓				✓		
Evening		✓		✓	✓		
Night	✓	✓		✓	✓	✓	

a Which was the driest day? _____

b On how many nights did it rain? _____

c When was the next dry spell after the period of rain that started on

Wednesday evening came to an end? _____

d During which part of each day (morning, afternoon, evening or night)

was it most often dry during that week? _____

3

Paper 5

1 $12 \times 3 = 30 +$ ___*6*___

2 $\frac{39}{3} =$ _____

3 $9 \times 9 =$ _____

4 $1.42 \times$ _____ $= 142$

5 Round these numbers to the nearest 100:

    a 466 _____   **c** 2990 _____

    b 239 _____   **d** 3591 _____

6 Draw a line between the numbers that have the same value:

    $\frac{1}{2}$ $\frac{75}{100}$

    $\frac{3}{4}$ 0.7

    $\frac{7}{10}$ 0.25

    $\frac{1}{4}$ $\frac{6}{12}$

7 What number comes next in these sequences?

    a 36, 33, 30, _____   **c** 45, 50, 55, _____

    b 104, 109, 114, 119, _____   **d** 200, 100, 50, _____

8 Convert these measurements to metres:

    a 2 km _____   **c** 350 cm _____

    b 5000 mm _____   **d** 0.04 km _____

9 What is the **perimeter** of a rectangle 7 cm wide and 16 cm long? _____

10 Put a tick inside the angles drawn below that are acute angles:

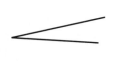 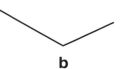

    a   **b**   **c**   **d**

11 If a bus leaves the station every 22 minutes, complete the departure times for the next two buses:

10:00, 10:22, 10:44, _____, _____

12 Share £360 between 9 people: _____

Which pattern completes the larger shape or grid? Underline the answer.

Example

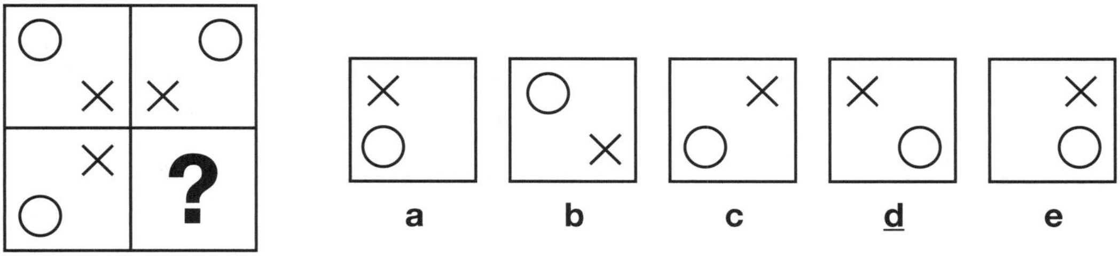

a   b   c   <u>d</u>   e

13

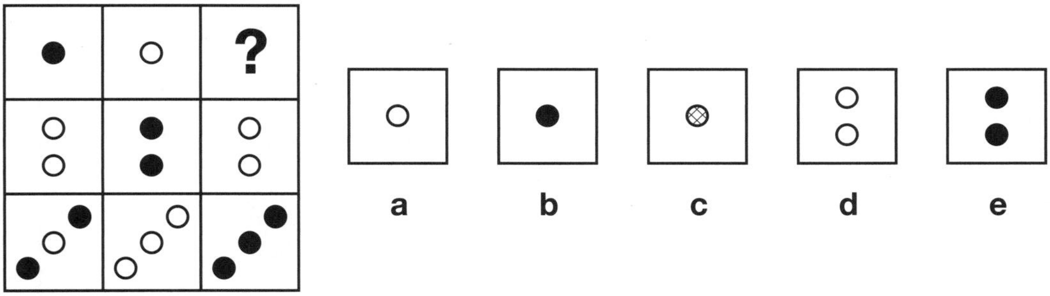

a   b   c   d   e

14

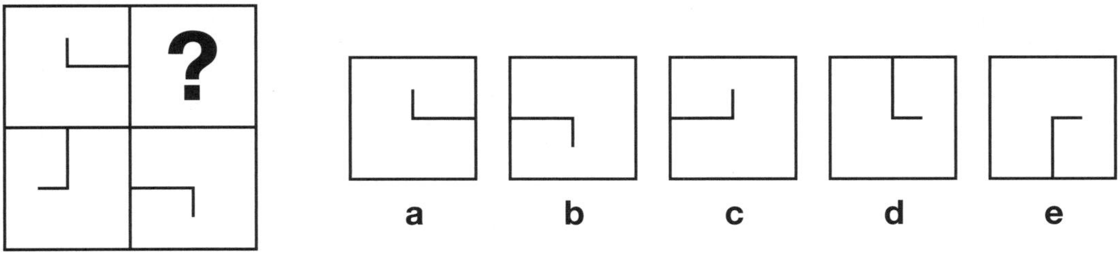

a   b   c   d   e

15

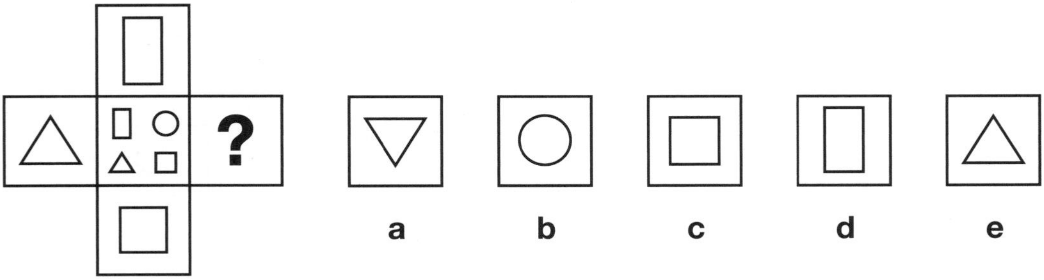

a   b   c   d   e

39

Which is the odd one out? Underline the answer.

Example

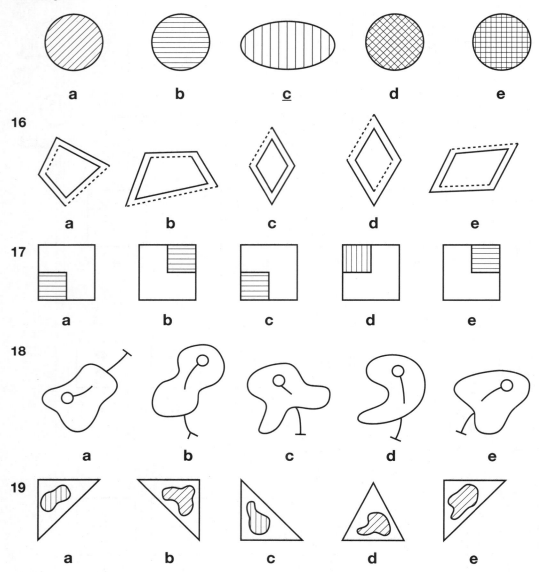

Which shape or pattern on the right belongs to the group on the left?
Underline the answer.

Example

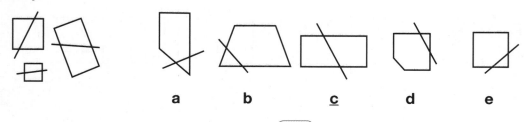

20

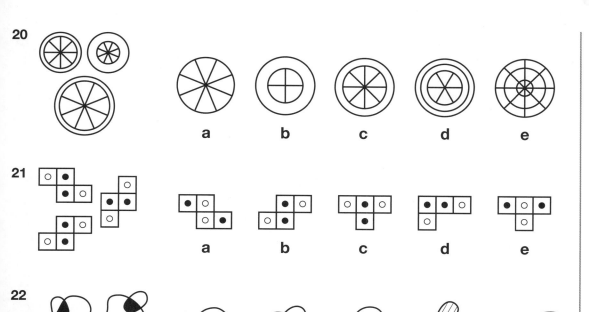

                a   b   c   d   e

21

                a   b   c   d   e

22

                a   b   c   d   e

Which code matches the shape or pattern given at the end of each line?
Underline the answer.

Example

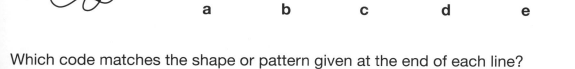

AX   BX   AY   CX   ?

               AX   BY   CY   BX   AY
                a   **<u>b</u>**   c   d   e

23

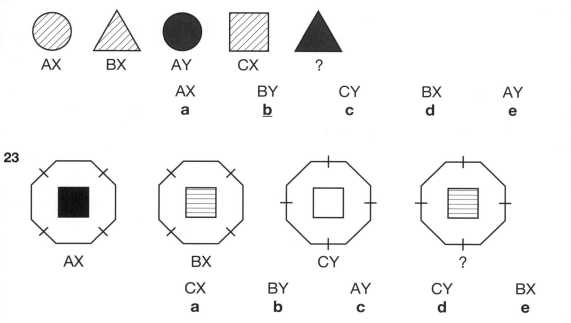

    AX   BX   CY   ?

      CX   BY   AY   CY   BX
       a   b   c   d   e

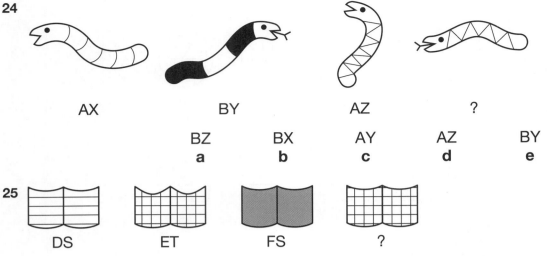

AX   BY   AZ   ?

	BZ	BX	AY	AZ	BY
	a	**b**	**c**	**d**	**e**

25

	DS	ET	FS	?	
	DT	FT	ET	ES	FS
	a	**b**	**c**	**d**	**e**

Which one comes next? Underline the answer.

Example

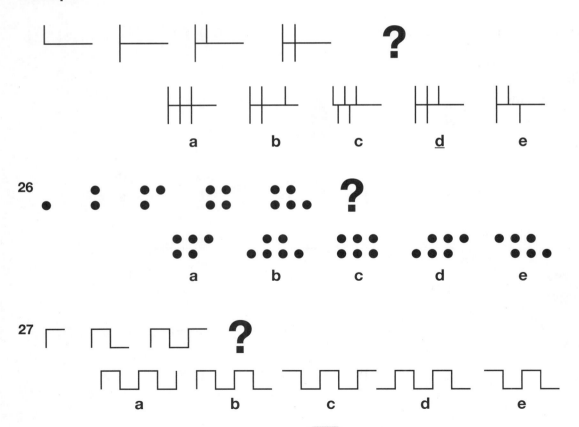

a   b   c   <u>d</u>   e

26

a   b   c   d   e

27

a   b   c   d   e

28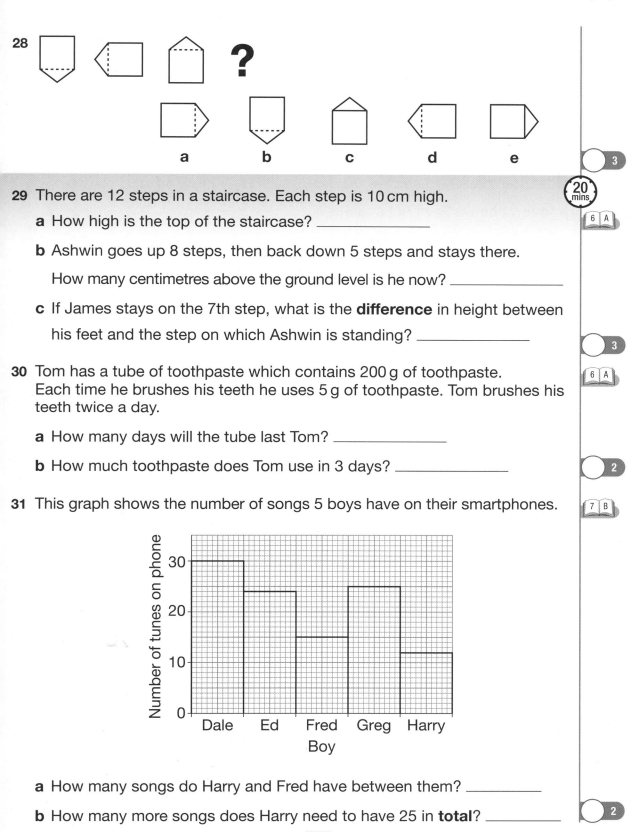

a   b   c   d   e

3

29 There are 12 steps in a staircase. Each step is 10 cm high.

⏱ 20 mins

6 A

    a How high is the top of the staircase? _____

    b Ashwin goes up 8 steps, then back down 5 steps and stays there.

    How many centimetres above the ground level is he now? _____

    c If James stays on the 7th step, what is the **difference** in height between

    his feet and the step on which Ashwin is standing? _____

3

30 Tom has a tube of toothpaste which contains 200 g of toothpaste.
Each time he brushes his teeth he uses 5 g of toothpaste. Tom brushes his
teeth twice a day.

6 A

    a How many days will the tube last Tom? _____

    b How much toothpaste does Tom use in 3 days? _____

2

31 This graph shows the number of songs 5 boys have on their smartphones.

7 B

(Bar graph: "Number of tunes on phone" (y-axis, 0 to 30) vs "Boy" (x-axis): Dale 30, Ed 24, Fred 15, Greg 25, Harry 12)

    a How many songs do Harry and Fred have between them? _____

    b How many more songs does Harry need to have 25 in **total**? _____

2

32 A bag of tile shapes was sorted. The red ones were separated from the other colours, and the square shapes from the other shapes. The numbers were recorded below. Complete the table and then answer the questions.

	Square	Not square	Total
Red	14	32	~~46~~
Not red	26	28	~~52~~
Total	~~40~~	~~60~~	

a How many shapes were not squares? _60_

b How many tiles were red? _46_

c How many tiles were sorted all together? _82_

$$\begin{array}{r} 14 \\ +32 \\ \hline 46 \end{array}$$

$$\begin{array}{r} +\begin{array}{c}32\\28\end{array} \\ \hline 46 \end{array}$$

3

33 Look carefully at the overlapping groups in the diagram below to work out the following answers:

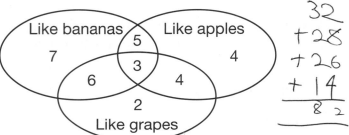

$$\begin{array}{r} 0 \\ 32 \\ +28 \\ +26 \\ +14 \\ \hline 82 \end{array}$$

a How many children like apples and bananas but not grapes? _~~8~~ 5_

b How many children like grapes but not apples or bananas? _2_

c How many children only like bananas? _7_

d How many children like all three fruits? _13_

e How many children like apples and grapes but not bananas? _4_

f How many like grapes and bananas but not apples? _6_

3

Now go to the Progress Chart to record your score! **Total** 45

Paper 6

1 25 × 5 = _____

2 24 ÷ _____ = 6

3 50 = 38 + _____ − 4

4 _____ − 6 = 35 + 2

5 What is the **perimeter** of a square with sides of 4.5 cm? _____

6 How many ml are there in 1.425 litres? _____

7 Write these **decimal** numbers in order of size:

   4.59   5.01   4.84   5.10   4.58

   _____ < _____ < _____ < _____ < _____

8 **Round** these numbers to the nearest 100:

   3752 _____   9549 _____   5050 _____   9959 _____

9 This machine adds 10, then divides by 2. What numbers have gone into it?

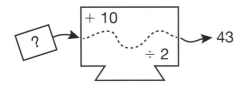

a _____

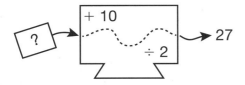

b _____

10 Complete this sentence by adding in the missing numbers:

   A **cube** has _____ square **faces**, _____ straight **edges** and

   _____ **vertices** (or corners).

11 Write $73\frac{1}{2}$ minutes as hours, minutes and seconds:

_____ hours   _____ minutes   _____ seconds

12 Toli recorded the amount of rain that fell during four weeks of his school holiday.

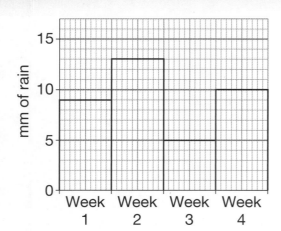

a How much rain fell in the first week? _____

b Which was the driest week? _____

c What was the **total** rainfall for the 4 weeks? _____

13 Here is part of a bus timetable.

	1st bus	2nd bus
Depot	8:00	8:30
Station	8:10	a
Park	8:18	b
Shops	8:32	c

If the time taken between the stops is the same as the 1st bus for every journey, complete the timetable for the 2nd bus leaving at 8:30.

a _____   **b** _____   **c** _____

d If the third bus on the route gets to the park at 9:28, when did it leave

the depot? _____

14 A variety box of 24 ice creams has 6 chocolate, 6 vanilla, 6 strawberry and the rest are mango.

  a How many mango ice creams are there in the box? _____

  b How many chocolate ice creams would there be in 5 variety boxes?

  _____

  c What **fraction** of each box is made up of vanilla ice creams? _____

15 A window measures 100 cm by 120 cm.

  a What is the **perimeter** of the window? _____

  Its shutters are 5 cm larger than the window on each side, as well as on the top and bottom.

  b What is the **perimeter** of the **area** covered by the shutters? _____

16 A candle burns at 1 cm per hour. The candle is 12 cm tall when it is lit at 3:30 pm.

  a How tall will the candle be at 5:30 pm? _____

  b How long will it take to burn up 5 cm of the candle? _____

  c What time will it be when the candle is 6 cm tall? _____

Which shape or pattern on the right belongs to the group on the left? Underline the answer.

Example

  a   **b**   **c**   **d**   **e**

17

  a   **b**   **c**   **d**   **e**

18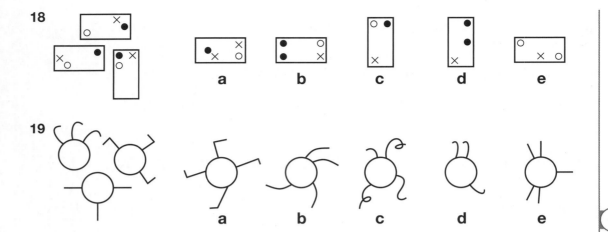

a   b   c   d   e

19

a   b   c   d   e

Which shape or pattern on the right completes the second pair in the same way as the first pair? Underline the answer.

Example

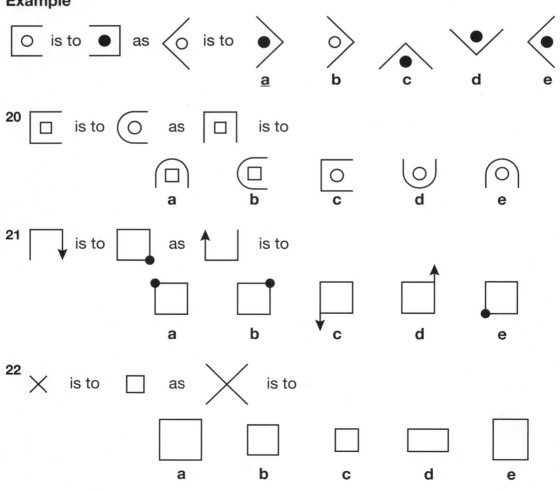

a   b   c   d   e

20 □ is to (○ as □ is to

a   b   c   d   e

21 is to as is to

a   b   c   d   e

22 ✕ is to □ as ✕ is to

a   b   c   d   e

23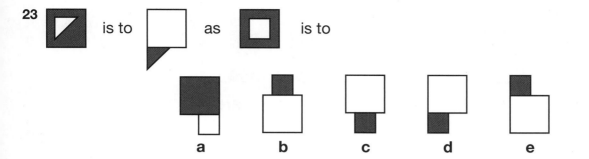

a b c d e

4

D 4

Which code matches the shape or pattern given at the end of each line?
Underline the answer.

Example

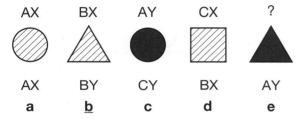

| AX | BX | AY | CX | ? |

| AX | BY | CY | BX | AY |
| a | **b** | c | d | e |

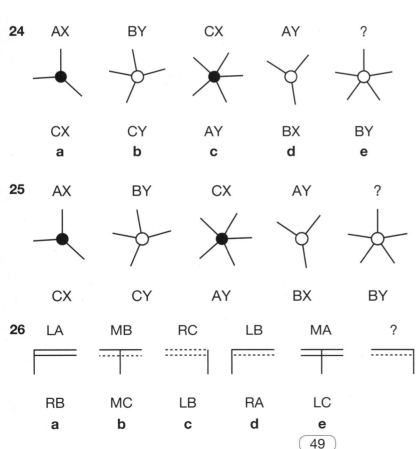

24

| AX | BY | CX | AY | ? |

| CX | CY | AY | BX | BY |
| a | b | c | d | e |

25

| AX | BY | CX | AY | ? |

| CX | CY | AY | BX | BY |

26

| LA | MB | RC | LB | MA | ? |

| RB | MC | LB | RA | LC |
| a | b | c | d | e |

49

27

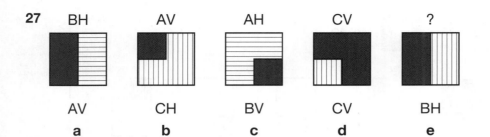

BH	AV	AH	CV	?
AV	CH	BV	CV	BH
a	**b**	**c**	**d**	**e**

Which pattern completes the larger shape or grid? Underline the answer.

Example

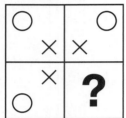

              a   **b**   **c**   **<u>d</u>**   **e**

28

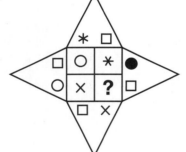

           a   **b**   **c**   **d**   **e**

29

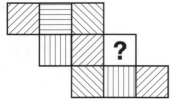

           a   **b**   **c**   **d**   **e**

30

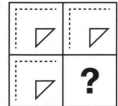

           a   **b**   **c**   **d**   **e**

4

3

Which shape or pattern on the right is a reflection of the one on the left?
Underline the answer.

Example

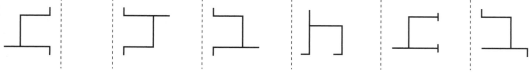

a   **<u>b</u>**   c   d   e

31

a   b   c   d   e

32

a   b   c   d   e

33

a   b   c   d   e

34

a   b   c   d   e

4

Now go to the Progress Chart to record your score!   Total 45

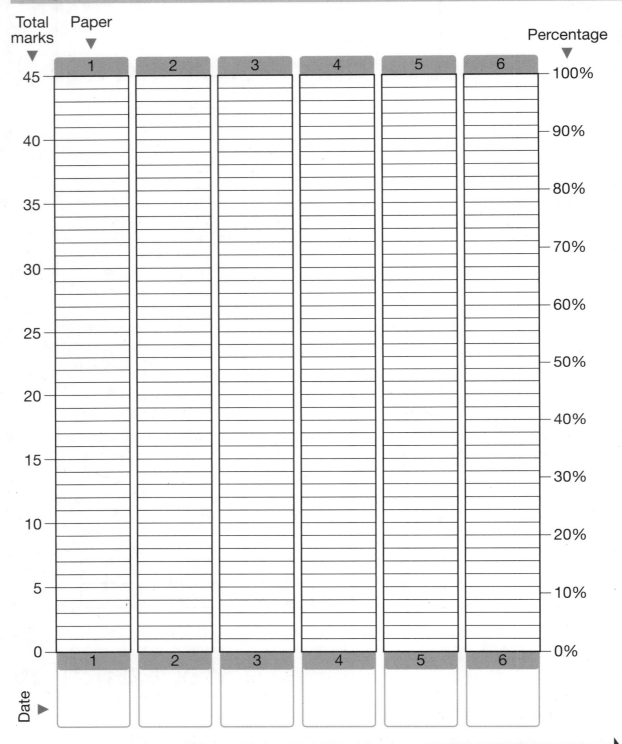

When you've finished the book use the **Next Steps Planner**